For Jason, my forever friend
~CF
For Anna, with all my love
~BC

Text Copyright © 2007 by Claire Freedman
Illustration Copyright © 2007 by Ben Cort
Published by arrangement with Simon & Schuster UK Ltd
1st Floor, 222 Gray's Inn Road, London, WC1X 8HB
A CBS Company

Dual language text copyright © 2011 Mantra Lingua
Audio copyright © 2011 Mantra Lingua
This edition 2011 All rights reserved
A CIP record for this book is available from the British Library
Mantra Lingua, Global House, 303 Ballards Lane, London, N12 8NP

www.mantralingua.com

Hear each page of this talking book narrated in many languages
with TalkingPEN! Then record your own versions.

Touch the arrow below with the TalkingPEN to start

Start   Info   English   Language

خلائی مخلوق کو جانگیے پسند ہیں
Aliens Love Underpants

Claire Freedman & Ben Cort

Urdu translation by Qamar Zamani

Mantra Lingua

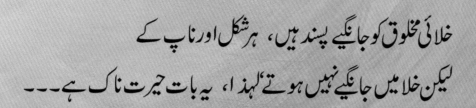

خلائی مخلوق کو جانگیے پسند ہیں، ہر شکل اور ناپ کے
لیکن خلا میں جانگیے نہیں ہوتے، لہذا، یہ بات حیرت ناک ہے۔۔۔

Aliens love underpants,
Of every shape and size.
But there are no underpants in space,
So here's a big surprise...

کہ جب وہ آتے ہیں زمین کی طرف ، تو تم سے ملنے نہیں آتے ۔۔۔
اُنہیں تو بس تمہارے جانگیے چاہئیں ، یہ بات تم نہیں جانتے ، ہے ، نا!

When aliens fly down to Earth, they don't come to meet YOU...
They simply want your underpants - I'll bet you never knew!

اُن کا آلہ چم چم چمکے اور آواز نکالے
جب وہ دیکھے دُور ہوا میں جانگیے سوکھنے والے ۔

Their spaceship's radar bleeps and blinks the moment that it sees
A washing line of underpants all flapping in the breeze.

وہ بن بلائے تمہارے پچھلے باغ میں اُتر آتے ہیں

"اُووووہ، جانگیے!" وہ خوشی سے ناچتے اورگاتے ہیں۔

They land in your back garden, though they haven't been invited.
"Oooooh, UNDERPANTS!" they chant, and dance around, delighted.

اُن کو پسند ہیں لال، ہرے اور نارنجی، نارنگی کی طرح

لیکن سب سے زیادہ دادی کی لمبی نیکر جس پر نشان ہیں گولی کی طرح۔

They like them red, they like them green, or orange like satsumas.
But best of all they love the sight of Granny's spotted bloomers.

اّمی کی گلابی لیس لگی نیکر چھپنے کے لئے اچھی جگہ ہے
اور دادا کا اُونی پاجامہ زن سے پھسلنے والی تختی ہے۔

Mum's pink frilly knickers are a perfect place to hide
And Grandpa's woolly longjohns make a super-whizzy slide.

In daring competitions, held up by just one peg,
They count how many aliens can squeeze inside each leg.

ایک دوسرے کو ہرانے کے شوق میں وہ ایک کھونٹی پر لٹک جاتے ہیں،
اور یہ گنتی ہوتی ہے کہ ایک ٹانگ میں کتنے لوگ سٹک جاتے ہیں۔

وہ جانگیے اپنے پیروں، سروں اور دوسری احمقانہ جگہوں پر چڑھاتے ہیں
اپنے خلائی جہاز سے جانگیے اُڑاتے ہیں اور اُلٹے جانگیوں کی دوڑ لگاتے ہیں!

They wear pants on their feet and heads and other silly places.
They fly pants from their spaceships and hold Upside-Down-Pant Races!

وہ جانگیے اپنے پیروں، سروں اور دوسری احمقانہ جگہوں پر چڑھاتے ہیں

جب وہ اُڑتے اور کلیاں مارتے پھرتے ہیں،
تو وہ واقعی پینٹی کا گل کھیلتے ہیں!
اور دوجانگیے ان سے لطف اُٹھاتے ہیں!

As they go zinging through the air,
it really is pants-tastic.
What fun the aliens can have
with pingy pants elastic!

یہ تمہارے پڑوسی کتے کا کام نہیں، نہ برابر والوں نے کھیل کھیلا ہے۔

جب جانگئے گم ہوتے ہیں تو یہ صرف خلائی مخلوق کا جھمیلا ہے!

It's not your neighbour's naughty dog, or next-door's funny game.
When underpants go missing, the ALIENS are to blame!

But quick! Mum's coming out to fetch the washing in at last.
Wheee! Off the aliens all zoom, they're used to leaving fast...

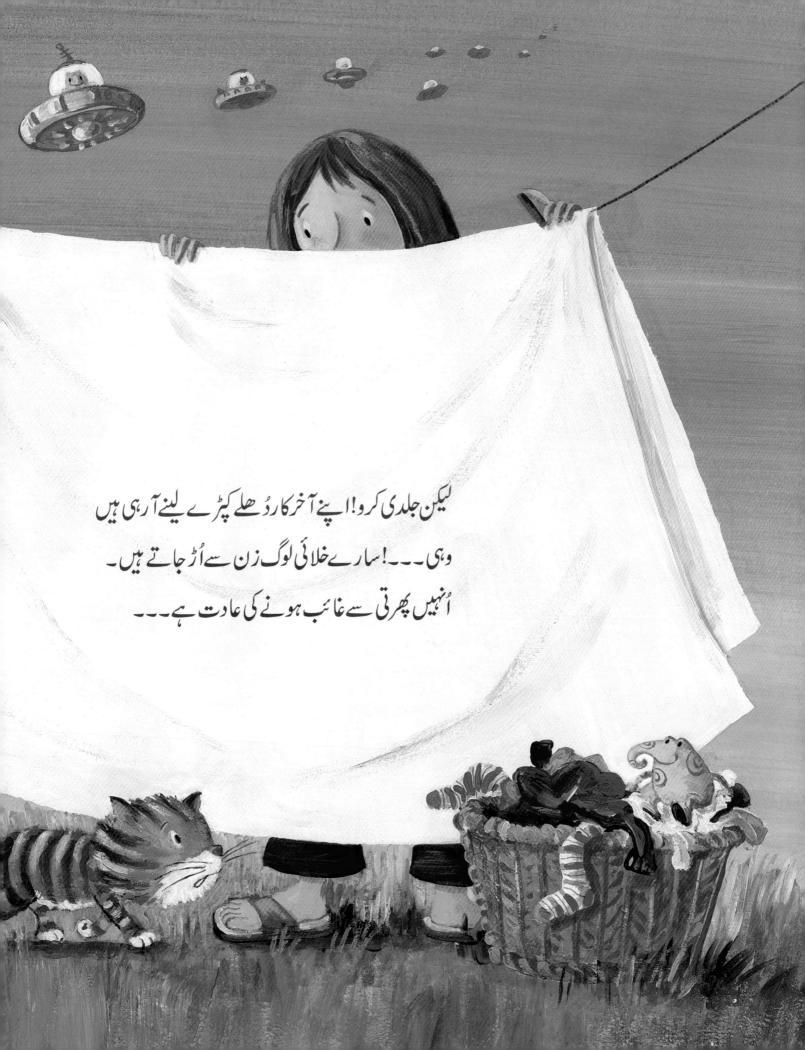

لیکن جلدی کرو! اپنے آخر کار دُھلے کپڑے لینے آ رہی ہیں
وہی۔۔۔! سارے خلائی لوگ زن سے اُڑ جاتے ہیں۔
اُنہیں پھرتی سے غائب ہونے کی عادت ہے۔۔۔

So when you put your pants on, freshly washed and nice and clean,
Just check in case an alien still lurks inside, unseen!

لہذا، اَب جب تم اپنا تازہ دُھلا جانگیہ پہنو،

تو ذرا اچھی طرح دیکھ لینا کہیں کوئی خلائی مخلوق اندر نہ گھوم رہی ہو، نظر سے اوجھل!